The PenDe.
Collectors Handbook
Third Edition

Stella M Ashbrook

Frank Salmon

Francis Joseph
London
1 870703-86-3

Acknowledgements

The third edition, who can believe it!!!?

Lots of interesting collecting has taken place since the last edition, and these new images will tell all. My thanks as always go to Jean, Doreen and Connie who always take an interest in my work. Arthur and Pauline Morley dedicated a lot of their time to me with my queries and ideas, and without their enthusiasm the PenDelfin product would not be one of the UK top collectables.

Warmest thanks go to Glenys and Sue Allen who again kindly gave up their time so we could photograph their amazing collection for the book. We took two days of their time this year - but a night out on the town with them both will be remembered by Frank and myself. Their collection is the most comprehensive in the UK if not the world and the care and attention they give their collection makes it inspiring to collectors.

Big thanks to all the staff at PenDelfin as they always go out of their way to help me and my staff during our Open Day and Auction. Ann Carney for her assistance throughout the year on pieces, dates etc. The collectors, who have forwarded information and images for inclusion in the book, you know who you are. Frank Salmon my Publisher who continues to promote PenDelfin via the bookshops. As 'Head Photographer' he has been a revelation, we have no excuse for missing deadlines now!!!

Lots of interesting facts and prices have been achieved over the last two years and I thank the Collectors for those. Without their continued interest and enthusiasm in the product the wonderful collecting club that PenDelfin is would not be possible.

My creative force is my Family, especially Maddie May, so sincere thanks to them.

© 2003 Francis Joseph Publications
Third Edition

Published in the UK by
Francis Joseph Publications
5 Southbrook Mews
London SE12 8LG
Telephone: 020 8318 9580

Typeset by E J Folkard Computer Services
199 Station Road, Crayford, Kent DA1 3QF

Printed in Great Britain

ISBN 1-870703-86-3

Contents

Introduction

Stella Ashbrook

A new and exciting layout to the third edition will hopefully make your collecting and identification a lot easier.

Having had more time to develop my interest in PenDelfin I have been astounded at the enormous interest this British Collectable still attracts. I do numerous talks to societies and charities and always take an assortment of PenDelfin with me to talk about, briefly talking about the history, the secondary market and the amazing collection available today. It always attracts questions and I have yet to do a talk were no one could remember PenDelfin of their childhood days. This addictive collectable can be sourced from various angles, whether you collect colour ways, rabbit models with variation, all pieces or just the membership pieces, there is something for everyone. I have noticed that the more serious collector has strengthened their collection by having a favourite and collecting the variation, ie: Lucy Pocket- Pockets, Uncle Soames - Waistcoats, Rolly - musical notes and colours, I could go on and on.

Over the last few years I have held two sales a year specialising in PenDelfin. Prices have been outstanding to average. The market place is such that late 2002 saw a slight dip in prices on the more common pieces, but my first sale in 2003 saw an upward turn. Collectable trends always change and we see upward and downward turns in all markets, but PenDelfin has been consistent and I put this down to an increase in collectors and a buoyant overseas market for the out of production pieces. We have seen Tony Green join PenDelfin as a Modeller and his work has brought in new ranges that tempt old and new collectors alike; the Policeman, Fireman and Harley and Davey were inspirational and just what the village needed. The models that will appeal to the younger generation will encourage them to start collecting and they will be the future of PenDelfin. It will be interesting to see over the next ten years where the collections have grown and how. Nostalgia plays a large part in any collecting field, and PenDelfin pieces given as a Birthday, Christening or Christmas present can lead onto huge collections taken up in the later years.

It is the Jubilee year for PenDelfin and celebrations have been going on throughout, with new pieces, special commissions and limited editions portray the wonderful array of PenDelfin products. Carltonware earlier this year was commissioned to produce a set of five original models in ceramic, modelled on the original family. We thought this would be an ideal start for new collectors, and established collections could house a smaller version. Jean Walmsley Heap produced a wonderful 'Jubilee Theatre' to celebrate the occasion, beautifully modelled as always, and a most appropriate way to mark the fifty years ahead. It is also ten years since the Family Circle was founded and so a model was made and named Dec&Ade (decade). Another product that has come out of the studios that will appeal to young and old collectors is the 'Paint Your Own Kit'. I thought this was a wonderful gift idea, I wouldn't let my three year old loose however (or myself for that matter). I am sure in the years to come though we will see some amazing paint effects - will they hold a premium I ask myself?

PenDelfin never ceases to amaze me, the family of rabbits that have grown over the years with their tales of village life are still growing and have adapted to the 21st Century without a hiccup. Jean and Doreen's ideas have developed with the collection, lending themselves to change and fashion. I am always chuckling with the very apt names on the pieces. Pressure to source products abroad to keep costs down have hit many collectable markets, PenDelfin has announced this year that their white wares are being sourced abroad due to increased manufacturing costs. We can take heart however that the painting of each piece will still be hand-done in Burnley and the designs still by Jean, Doreen and Tony.
Happy collecting and a big thank you to all the collectors as it's down to you PenDelfin is here today.

Stella

Special thanks to Glenys & Sue

Repaints and Restorations

Like all ceramics or stonecraft, there are vulnerable elements on the PenDelfin range. Because of the stonecraft's consistency the models will be prone to chips or even the loss of an ear or arm if they are knocked over. It is therefore not uncommon to see older pieces with some repair or restoration to damage. If this is the case, the work done or repair made does not necessarily maintain the value of a perfect original. A piece which has a small chip or glaze flakes can in many ways be more desirable than a restored piece, due to its originality. Repaints are obvious to the eye as they don't have that same feel about them, even when painted in the same colourway. Age shows on a model and adds to its charm, and to a collector it doesn't matter if a model that is 30 years old bears some sort of fault or other. However, a genuine model that has weathered the mantlepiece, the test of time and probably numerous moves, is most desirable in perfect condition.

Certain pieces are prone to damage because of being top heavy. For example, 'Shiner', Dungaree Father Rabbit, Megan the Harp, (her harp is prone to the top being chipped,) and Robert, Satchel, (who has more often than not got repaired ears).

PenDelfin have a service where they restore and repaint models at the studios. In order to do this they strip the figure or the model completely and more or less start from stratch. This makes the figure look like new when completed, but it somehow seems quite odd to see an old piece in new paints, the once subtle tones have been replaced by the bolder shades which are present today.

Cauldron Witch, Left: Stripped ready for re-painting and right, how it should look.

Colour Listings and Variations

I attempted to do a colour variation index in the last edition, however quite a lot of feedback has come back to me, because if I have missed a colour a lot of people have presumed it's a rare shade. In this edition I am doing it the other way, I am listing the Rare Colour shades on models. A model not listed means that what ever shade it is painted in is available via the secondary market. Please forward information to me if I have missed pieces that have variations or colour changes. Also note, any model painted with green eyes, is more than likely to have been painted by Jean.

AUNT AGATHA	She is particularly saleable in Turquoise and Pale Blue. Lilac is rare.
BARNEY	Red/Pink shoes.
BARNEY BUNDLE	Black and White (500 made limited edition).
BLAZER	Green flag.
BONGO	1st version coloured drum.
CHA CHA	Lilac, Green or Turquoise.
COOKIE	Pale Blue.
DRIFTER	five with Blue dolphins and Silver Anchor.
EUCLID	Blank board.

Connie and Jean discussing colourways.

FATHER DUNGAREE	Lilac or with any distinct pattern to dungarees, other than flora.
FATHER KIPPER TIE	Lilac or with any distinct pattern to tie, other than dots, lines, flora.
FLAGMAKER	Grey dress (100 approx made).
HOLLY	Red, also a smaller base to first version.
JIM LAD	Rubber band, no band, patch.
JINGLE	Small and large bell.
LUCY POCKET	Lilac, also pockets with unusual patterns, ie; snail.
MEGAN THE HARP	Yellow/Black.
MIDGE	Three crumbs.
MIKE (1ST Version)	Cuff matched colour and pocket.
MIKE (2nd Version)	One colour beige, self coloured like jacket.
MIKE (3rd Version)	Yellow wash.
MOPPIT	Lime green (made for the Canadian market).
MOTHER (1st Version)	Lilac - her skirt is always rarer if painted with motifs or animals.
MOTHER (1ST Version	Tassels to shawl or scalloped skirt.
NOEL	Christmas colours (Red).
PETE	Green shoe (made for Canadian market).
POPPET	2 Weave or 3 Weave variation.
PICNIC ISLAND	Black kettle.
RAMBLER	Tweed, Red.
ROBERT SATCHEL	Lilac.
ROLLY	Three notes
ROSA	Blue and Black, Turquoise, different shade of green ribbon.
SANDIE	Five with blue anchor.
SCOUT	Look out for two sausages in pan.
SHINER	Full bruise is harder to find, pockets are also decorated, rare shade Lilac.
SLEDGER	Green.
SOLO	Black.
TAMMY	Small or large version, silver or gilt collar.
TEDDY	Green.
TIMBER STAND	Green.
UNCLE SOAMES	Trousers Black - Common.
	Trousers Brown - Rare.
	Trousers Blue - Very Rare.
	Trousers Mushroom - Rare.
	Waistcoats all shades.
VILLAGE POND	Red wellies.
WHOPPER	Silver Brim.

Pixie Bods

One of the most appealing things about Pixie Bod is its simplicity. Such a simple idea which proved to be highly commercial in its time. Introduced in 1965 from a inspired idea of Jeans, she was recovering at the time from a bout of flu. The initial thought was to invent a decorative support for trailing foliage or flora. Jean designed the heads and feet and the flexible body was made up of pipe cleaners with felt jerkins and caps. The actual assembling of the Bods was the problem, they were so fiddly especially applying the two felt buttons on the jerkins. Many examples were rejected due to poor preparation and Dorian took to overseeing other batches to reduce the amount of rejects. The packaging was fun too, with black printed silhouettes of pixies in a plant, on a desk or in the car, these were set against cream card and the Pixie Bod was then attached and placed in a window box so it could be viewed. To display the Bods initially the "Large House" was built, this had Pixie Bods fixed on the sides and in the window, that's prior to the Rabbits moving in and Barney. Another display piece was the Pixie Bod Caravan, this was all handmade, down to the furniture and fittings. This display piece was first exhibited at the International Trade Fair in Blackpool in 1965. Approximately only 14 examples were made and when they do come up for sale they realise very high prices. The piano known as the Honky Tonk Piano, now in the range and used by Thumper was initially made for the Pixie Bods. Early Piano's have an elaborate scrolling pattern to the sides.

The rarest of all the Bods is the Girl Bod which has bobbed hair. The local hairdresser knew a wig-maker who supplied the miniature styles of hair in shades of Strawberry Blonde, Brown and Black. Jean however with her artistic nature captured the characters perfectly by designing their costumes, it took her back to her Art College days.

Two years of sticky fingers, felt trimmings and numerous rejects saw the Pixie Bods retire. Thirty One years on they still capture everyone's imagination.

The Wonderful Imagination of Jean Walmsley-Heap

Jean's wonderful illustrations for Books have created a lot of interest over the last few years, collectors have searched high and low for copies of *Dingleflop Chimes*, *Little Round House* and the elusive *Cherry Pie*.

The first book to be published with Jean's illustrations was *The Little Pink Rabbit*, by Eileen Graham, a delightful paper back about would you belief a Rabbit - pure coincidence. Jean told me once of her joy at having written and illustrated in those early years, and if the rabbit family hadn't burrowed into her heart she would still be writing today. Her work is an inspiration to all.

The following information has been sourced since the last edition, and you can find Jeans wonderful illustrations in all.

Little Round House by Marion St-John Webb, published 1956 by Collins.
On a Pin Cushion by Mary de Morgan, published 1950
Before Bed Stories by Maud Morrin, published 1950
More Before Bed Stories by Maud Morrin, published 1957
Mr Papingay's Ship by Marion St. John Webb, published 1957.
Cherry Pie by Jean Walmsley Heap, still to be published.
The Pink Rabbit by Eileen Graham
Dingleflop Chimes by Jean Walmsley Heap, published 1949
Dingleflop Moon by Jean Walmsley Heap, published 1953
Little Folks Annual, Collins, published 1959
Childrens Annual, Collins, published 1956
Girls Annual, Collins, published 1954
Childrens Annual, Collins, published 1958
Childrens Annual, A surprise for Santa, published 1961

There will be many more Annuals and Books that Jean would have applied her pen, so keep your eyes peeled, all information for future reference would be gratefully received.

The 'Pookie' Tale

On 12th July 1997, the *Daily Mail Weekend Magazine* had a feature on William Hope Collins and his romance with Ivy Wallace. Ivy Wallace was a children's author and in her heyday sold over a million books. Her main character was a rabbit called "Pookie". This lively rabbit with wings got into all kinds of mischief and with other imaginary characters filled numerous books. Where does PenDelfin come in you wonder? Well, on one of the photographs featured in the article, Ivy Wallace is at her desk drawing, all the characters are seated around her, as well as a rabbit with wings. The rabbit seated with Ivy was made by Jean Walmsley Heap. Having seen this article you can imagine the response and the questions which have been asked. How a PenDelfin "Dungaree" Father rabbit came to be "Pookie"? or how "Pookie" came to be Dungaree Father Rabbit? I first heard the name "Pookie" at the PenDelfin Studios when a gentleman came in with a larger than normal Dungaree Father Rabbit, he said it was a "Pookie". I asked Jean about "Pookie" and she told me how she had been asked to model a rabbit for Ivy Wallace that would be the image of "Pookie", which she did. However the rabbit that Jean modelled had teeth and Ivy Wallace rejected it, as her "Pookie" didn't have the characteristic buck teeth of a rabbit. So what we know as a Dungaree Father

Pookie Style Dungaree Father Rabbit.

Rabbit was shelved for a couple of years until it was mentioned to Jean that he deserved a wife!

The first Dungaree Father Rabbits are larger and have a bulbous bottom and large feet, the colourways are bright and there is shading between the eyes and in the ears is a pinky colour (see colour photo page 00).

"Pookie" actually never went into production as a figure, he stayed within the immaginal stories that Ivy Wallace wrote, It does make me wonder however if Jean had modelled the rabbit without teeth whether there would be a rabbit family at all, or whether we would be coveting the traditional witches and figural subjects that were the models prior to the rabbit family. The "Pookie" books have been reprinted, this time in colour by a family publishing company run by Ivy's two daughters.

The titles of the Original Pookie Books:
Pookie, Pookie and his Shop, Pookie believes in Santa Claus, Pookie in Wonderland, Pookie puts the World Right, Pookie and the Swallows and *Pookies Big Day*

Serious collectors have original examples of these books, as they reflect a small part in PenDelfin's History.

Care and Security of your Collection

Today's society in many ways dictates what precautions against theft must be taken. Because like any other collectable PenDelfin is a commercial commodity thought must be given to its security. A full listing of your models with colourway identification would suffice, making note of out of production pieces. This list should be duplicated and one sent to your insurance company and the other kept in a secure place or in the hands of your solicitor. Prevention of crime is half the battle and key points should be noted.

- Do not place models on windowsills in view of passers by.
- When away on holiday pack up the models of high value and put in a more secure place.
- Have photographs of your collection.
- Endeavour to keep the extent of your collection and its value to yourself.

Caring for your collection is just as important as making it secure. To ensure a piece keeps its value it must be a perfect example. PenDelfin because of its texture is prone to damage and therefore keeping models in quantity can be nerve racking. One hint is to keep the models well spaced apart on shelves to prevent chips occurring. Other sources harmful to a collection are sun, water and direct heat, so keeping models away from damp, sunshine and fires can help maintain the glaze of the models for years.

If models are subjected to the elements erosion of the glaze and discoloration becomes obvious and the value depreciates. To keep your collection clean a light dusting on a regular basis will suffice.

The hunt for Little Thrifty goes on - and Old Meg must be with him

Five years on and still no sign of Little Thrifty. A character that was prominent in the Children's Corner at the Burnley Building Society. Stories by Jean Walmsley Heap centred around the character of Little Thrifty and a large model of him was commissioned. It was the largest model made by Jean, the model produced problems in casting and no other models on that scale were attempted again.

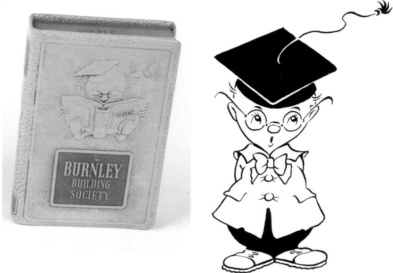

A money book was found however which was from the Burnley Building Society, so things are out there that have a direct link to the first steps of PenDelfin.

OLD MEG Wall Plaque, well I know of two examples, however I have never had the opportunity to sell via auction the wonderful image of Old Meg. She is one of the most sought after pieces on the secondary market and I would be overjoyed to sell her through a specialist sale - SO if anyone out there wants to test the market place and see her potential - let me know. Jean can't remember how many were made, but it would only be a handful, there must be another out there somewhere!

Right: Old Meg plaque, very rare, introduced 1953, withdrawn 1954, £5000-£8000/$4995-$6995.

Backstamps and Labels

The dating of labels is very difficult as the most accurate information was contained in records that were destroyed in the fire of the mid-1980s. Therefore some of our guides are only approximate.

The labels have common features. They are generally paper with a black background and gold inscription. However, they come in various shapes which incorporate a variety of wording which may or may not include:

PenDelfin name
Registered Trademark
Handpainted Stonecraft
Made in England
Characters Name.

On early models 'designed by Jean Walmsley Heap' may be inscribed as with the gilt Butterfly label.

The Membership Gifts and Model of the Year figures bear black circular labels with gold inscriptions.

The Pre 1960s plaques, for example **Pendle Witch** or the **Fairy Shop** have handpainted titles and Jean Walmsley Heap's signature. These are not backed with baize.

Handpainted signature and Logo, titled, painted in red circa 1954-1958. Some pieces have subsequently been signed by Jean Walmsley Heap.

Gilt Butterfly label label found on larger, old retired pieces such as Old Mother, Original Grandstand and Bandstand. Circa 1956-1960.

Label found on Cornish Prayer along with traditional label, circa 1962-1965.

White artist palette label with gold print. Found on Rocky, Wakey, Megan, Father and others. Origin unknown, circa 1960-1962.

Rectangular gold (circa 1958-1970) or silver (circa 1958-1960) foil label with black lettering found on smaller, old retired pieces such as Gussie, Original Robert, Shiner. Also found on a few larger ones as well such as Uncle Soames.

Three labels based on the artist palette label format: The first two are traditional black labels with gold foil border, containing the name of the piece. It is found on most pieces. Circa 1960-1980s. Far right has "Regd Design" instead of the name of the piece and is found on some early models.

Black label but without gold foil border. Found on a few of older retired pieces.

Triangle shaped label, black with white print.

Listings and Price Guide

Rabbits

The Rabbit Family began with five, coming to life,Father (dungaree), Mother, Robert (satchel), Margot and Midge (biscuit). Many colourways can be found on thse pieces because of the less conformed use of paints as there is today. Obviously there are certain models which are the exception though, for example 'Blazer' with green flag, 'Uncle Soames' with brown trousers, 'Rambler' yellow hat, etc. Kipper Tie 'Father' has a variety of ties in all shades and designs, 'Mother' has various designs to her skirt, and there's many more. Its keeping your eyes open and noticing the smaller details that will enable you to have an unusual example in your collection. Happy Hunting!

Ahoy-Boy

Designer:
Jean Walmsley Heap

Size:
3"

Production Period:
1998-Cur

Market Value:
RRP

Angelo

Designer:
Jean Walmsley Heap

Size:
4"

Production Period:
1990-2000

Market Value:
£40-£60/$60-$105

Auctioneer

Ltd edition piece of 1000

Designer:
Doreen Noel Roberts

Size:
5"

Production Period:
2001

Market Value:
£100-£150/$150-$263

Aunt Agatha

Designer:
Jean Walmsley Heap

Size:
8″

Production Period:
1963-1965

Market Value:
£1200-£1800/$1800-$3150

Aunt Ruby

Limited Edition of 10000

Designer:
Jean Walmsley Heap

Size:
8″

Production Period:
1993-1996

Market Value:
£150-£200/$225-$350

Barney

Green Towel

Designer:
Doreen Noel Roberts

Size:
3″

Production Period:
1967-Cur

Market Value:
RRP

Barney

Blue Towel

Designer:
Doreen Noel Roberts

Size:
3″

Production Period:
1967-Cur

Market Value:
RRP

Barney

Red Towel

Designer:
Doreen Noel Roberts

Size:
3″

Production Period:
1967-Cur

Market Value:
RRP

Barney Bundle

Red Hat and Scarf

Designer:
Doreen Noel Roberts

Size:
3″

Production Period:
1997-Cur

Market Value:
RRP

Barney Bundle

Blue Hat and Scarf

Designer:
Doreen Noel Roberts

Size:
3″

Production Period:
1997-Cur

Market Value:
RRP

Barney Bundle

Black and white version (Limited edition of 500)

Designer:
Doreen Noel Roberts

Size:
3″

Production Period:
1998 only

Market Value:
£120-£180/$180-$315

Barrow Boy

Designer:
Jean Walmsley Heap

Size:
5″

Production Period:
1968-2001

Market Value:
£20-£40/$30-$70

Biff

Designer:
Doreen Noel Roberts

Size:
4″

Production Period:
2000-Cur

Market Value:
RRP

Big Spender

Designer:
Doreen Noel Roberts

Size:
5″

Production Period:
1996-2000

Market Value:
£25-£50/$38-$88

Birdie

Designer:
Jean Walmsley Heap

Size:
5″

Production Period:
1987-Cur

Market Value:
RRP

Blaster

Designer:
TG
Size:
4″
Production Period:
2000-Cur
Market Value:
RRP

Blazer

Red
Designer:
Jean Walmsley Heap
Size:
4″
Production Period:
1996-Cur
Market Value:
RRP

Blazer

Green (approx 400 produced)
Designer:
Jean Walmsley Heap
Size:
4″
Production Period:
1996 only
Market Value:
£200-£300/$300-$525

Bliss

Designer:
TG
Size:
4″
Production Period:
2000-Cur
Market Value:
RRP

Blossom

Designer:
Doreen Noel Roberts
Size:
4″
Production Period:
1984-1989
Market Value:
£50-£80/$75-$140

Blunder

Designer:
TG
Size:
5″
Production Period:
2001-Cur
Market Value:
RRP

Bobby

Designer:
Doreen Noel Roberts

Size:
5"

Production Period:
1996-Cur

Market Value:
RRP

Bongo

Black jacket, green drum

Designer:
Jean Walmsley Heap

Size:
3"

Production Period:
1964-1987

Market Value:
£50-£80/$75-$140

Bongo

Blue jacket, black drum

Designer:
Jean Walmsley Heap

Size:
3"

Production Period:
1964-1987

Market Value:
£50-£80/$75-$140

Bongo

Green jacket, red drum

Designer:
Jean Walmsley Heap

Size:
3"

Production Period:
1964-1987

Market Value:
£50-£80/$75-$140

Boswell

Designer:
Jean Walmsley Heap

Size:
4"

Production Period:
1972-Cur

Market Value:
RRP

Bronco

Designer:
TG

Size:
4"

Production Period:
2002

Market Value:
RRP

Bunch

Designer:
Jean Walmsley Heap

Production Period:
2000-Cur

Market Value:
RRP

Busker

Designer:
Doreen Noel Roberts

Size:
5″

Production Period:
1997-Cur

Market Value:
RRP

Butterfingers

Designer:
Doreen Noel Roberts

Size:
3″

Production Period:
1991-Cur

Market Value:
RRP

Captain Musket

Designer:
TG

Size:
5″

Production Period:
1999-Cur

Market Value:
RRP

Casanova

Designer:
Jean Walmsley Heap

Size:
3″

Production Period:
1982-1998

Market Value:
£30-£40 / $45-$70

Cha Cha

Designer:
Jean Walmsley Heap

Size:
5″

Production Period:
1959-1961

Market Value:
£1200-£1800 / $1800-$3150

Charlotte

Designer:
Doreen Noel Roberts

Size:
4″

Production Period:
1990-1992

Market Value:
£80-£120/$120-$210

Cheeky

Designer:
Doreen Noel Roberts

Size:
4″

Production Period:
1996-1998

Market Value:
£40-£60/$60-$105

Chirpy

Designer:
Doreen Noel Roberts

Size:
4″

Production Period:
1989-1992

Market Value:
£70-£100/$105-$175

Chuck

Designer:
Doreen Noel Roberts

Size:
4″

Production Period:
2000-Cur

Market Value:
RRP

Clanger

Red jacket

Designer:
Jean Walmsley Heap

Size:
4″

Production Period:
1983-1998

Market Value:
£30-£50/$45-$88

Clanger

Blue jacket

Designer:
Jean Walmsley Heap

Size:
4″

Production Period:
1983-1998

Market Value:
£30-£50/$45-$88

Cookie

Designer:
Doreen Noel Roberts

Size:
4″

Production Period:
1995-2000

Market Value:
£30-£50/$45-$88

Cousin Beau

Designer:
Doreen Noel Roberts

Size:
4″

Production Period:
1993-1999

Market Value:
£30-£50/$45-$88

Cracker

Designer:
Doreen Noel Roberts

Size:
6″

Production Period:
2000-Cur

Market Value:
RRP

Crocker

Designer:
Doreen Noel Roberts

Size:
5″

Production Period:
1980-1989

Market Value:
£50-£100/$75-$175

Dandy

Designer:
Doreen Noel Roberts

Size:
4″

Production Period:
1981-Cur

Market Value:
RRP

Dasher

Designer:
Doreen Noel Roberts

Size:
7″Long

Production Period:
1996-Cur

Market Value:
RRP

Dawn

Designer:
Doreen Noel Roberts

Size:
4″

Production Period:
2002-2003

Market Value:
£30-£50/$45-$88

Dec & Ade

Anniversary Piece

Designer:
Jean Walmsley Heap

Size:
6″

Production Period:
2003-Cur

Market Value:
RRP

Deputy

Designer:
TG

Size:
4″

Production Period:
2001-Cur

Market Value:
RRP

Digit

Designer:
Doreen Noel Roberts

Size:
3″

Production Period:
1991-Cur

Market Value:
RRP

Dobbin

Designer:
Jean Walmsley Heap

Size:
4″

Production Period:
1995-Cur

Market Value:
RRP

Dodger

Designer:
Jean Walmsley Heap

Size:
4″

Production Period:
1964-1995

Market Value:
£30-£40/$45-$70

Dot Com

Rare one only piece, sold at auction on behalf of Charity.

Designer:
Jean Walmsley Heap

Size:
4"

Production Period:
2002

Market Value:
£4000-£6000/$6000-$10500

Drifter

Designer:
Jean Walmsley Heap

Size:
4"

Production Period:
1998-Cur

Market Value:
RRP

Drifter

Special edition (Dolphins) 500 made

Designer:
Jean Walmsley Heap

Size:
4"

Production Period:
2000-2000

Market Value:
£120-£180/$180-$315

Picture
Unavailable

Drifter

Special edition (Silver Anchor) only 5 made

Designer:
Jean Walmsley Heap

Size:
4"

Production Period:
2000-2000

Market Value:
£200-£300/$300-$525

Duffy

Designer:
Jean Walmsley Heap

Size:
4"

Production Period:
1989-Cur

Market Value:
RRP

Euclid

Designer:
Jean Walmsley Heap

Size:
3"

Production Period:
1989-Cur

Market Value:
RRP

Euclid

Blank Board

Designer:
Jean Walmsley Heap

Size:
3″

Production Period:
1989-Cur

Market Value:
RRP

Euclid

One off

Designer:
Jean Walmsley Heap

Size:
3″

Production Period:
1989-Cur

Market Value:
RRP

Father

Standard Dungaree

Designer:
Jean Walmsley Heap

Size:
8″

Production Period:
1955-1960

Market Value:
£800-£1200/$1200-$2100

Father

Dungaree colourway

Designer:
Jean Walmsley Heap

Size:
8″

Production Period:
1955-1960

Market Value:
£800-£1200/$1200-$2100

Father

Unusual horse painted dungarees

Designer:
Jean Walmsley Heap

Size:
8″

Production Period:
1955-1960

Market Value:
£800-£1200/$1200-$2100

Father

Kipper Tie

Designer:
Jean Walmsley Heap

Size:
8″

Production Period:
1960-1970

Market Value:
£400-£600/$600-$1050

Father

Kipper Tie

Designer:
Jean Walmsley Heap

Size:
8″

Production Period:
1960-1970

Market Value:
£400-£600/$600-$1050

Father

Designer:
Jean Walmsley Heap

Size:
8″

Production Period:
1977-Cur

Market Value:
RRP

Fireman

Designer:
TG

Size:
4″

Production Period:
2001

Market Value:
RRP

Flagmaker

Colour change by artist 100 made

Designer:
TG

Size:
5″

Production Period:
2001-2001

Market Value:
£200-£300/$300-$525

Flagmaker

Canadian

Designer:
TG

Size:
5″

Production Period:
2001

Market Value:
RRP

Flagmaker

Scotland

Designer:
TG

Size:
5″

Production Period:
2001

Market Value:
RRP

Flagmaker

England

Designer:
TG

Size:
5"

Production Period:
2001

Market Value:
RRP

Flagmaker

Wales

Designer:
TG

Size:
5"

Production Period:
2001

Market Value:
RRP

Flagmaker

USA

Designer:
TG

Size:
5"

Production Period:
2001

Market Value:
RRP

Forty Winks

Designer:
Doreen Noel Roberts

Size:
5"Long

Production Period:
1993-1995

Market Value:
£60-£100/$90-$175

Gussie

Designer:
Jean Walmsley Heap

Size:
3"

Production Period:
1960-1968

Market Value:
£300-£400/$450-$700

Happy

Designer:
TG

Size:
5"

Production Period:
2003-Cur

Market Value:
RRP

Harley & Davey

Designer:
TG

Size:
6″

Production Period:
2001

Market Value:
RRP

Holly

*Red colourway 1st Version base of
Skate small approx 150 made*

Designer:
Doreen Noel Roberts

Size:
4″

Market Value:
£0/$0

Holly

1st edition

Designer:
Doreen Noel Roberts

Size:
4″

Production Period:
1999

Market Value:
£60-£100/$90-$175

Holly

Designer:
Doreen Noel Roberts

Size:
4″

Production Period:
1999-Cur

Market Value:
RRP

Honey

Designer:
Doreen Noel Roberts

Size:
4″

Production Period:
1989-1992

Market Value:
£40-£60/$60-$105

Hot Pot

Designer:
Doreen Noel Roberts

Size:
4″

Production Period:
1999-2003

Market Value:
£30-£50/$45-$88

Humphrey Go-Kart

Designer:
Jean Walmsley Heap

Size:
5″

Production Period:
1988-1994

Market Value:
£80-£120/$120-$210

Jacky

Designer:
Doreen Noel Roberts

Size:
3″

Production Period:
1992-Cur

Market Value:
RRP

Jim Lad

Designer:
Doreen Noel Roberts

Size:
5″

Production Period:
1986-1992

Market Value:
£80-£120/$120-$210

Jim Lad

Designer:
Doreen Noel Roberts

Size:
5″

Production Period:
1986-1992

Market Value:
£80-£120/$120-$210

Jim Lad

Designer:
Doreen Noel Roberts

Size:
5″

Production Period:
1986-1992

Market Value:
£80-£120/$120-$210

Jingle

Designer:
Doreen Noel Roberts

Size:
3″

Production Period:
1985-1992

Market Value:
£80-£120/$120-$210

Little Big Paddle

Canadian Exclusive

Designer:
TG

Size:
5″

Production Period:
2001-2002

Market Value:
£130-£180/$195-$315

Little Brave

Canadian Exclusive

Designer:
Doreen Noel Roberts

Size:
6″

Production Period:
2001-2002

Market Value:
£100-£150/$150-$263

Little Mo

Designer:
Doreen Noel Roberts

Size:
2″

Production Period:
1986-1994

Market Value:
£50-£80/$75-$140

Lucy Pocket

Designer:
Jean Walmsley Heap

Size:
4″

Production Period:
1960-1967

Market Value:
£100-£180/$150-$315

Lucy Pocket

Designer:
Jean Walmsley Heap

Size:
4″

Production Period:
1960-1967

Market Value:
£100-£180/$150-$315

Margot

Pleated skirt

Designer:
Jean Walmsley Heap

Size:
4″

Production Period:
1956-1957

Market Value:
£250-£350/$375-$613

Margot

Unusual painted skirt

Designer:
Jean Walmsley Heap

Size:
4″

Production Period:
1956-1957

Market Value:
£250-£350/$375-$613

Margot

Semi-pleated

Designer:
Jean Walmsley Heap

Size:
4″

Production Period:
1956-1959

Market Value:
£150-£200/$225-$350

Margot

Straight

Designer:
Jean Walmsley Heap

Size:
4″

Production Period:
1957-1967

Market Value:
£100-£150/$150-$263

Maud

Designer:
Jean Walmsley Heap

Size:
3″

Production Period:
1967-1978

Market Value:
£120-£200/$180-$350

Maud

Designer:
Jean Walmsley Heap

Size:
3″

Production Period:
1967-1978

Market Value:
£120-£200/$180-$350

Megan The Harp

Designer:
Jean Walmsley Heap

Size:
4″

Production Period:
1960-1967

Market Value:
£250-£450/$375-$788

Megan The Harp

Designer:
Jean Walmsley Heap

Size:
4″

Production Period:
1960-1967

Market Value:
£250-£450/$375-$788

Midge

1 Crumb

Designer:
Jean Walmsley Heap

Size:
3″

Production Period:
1956-1965

Market Value:
£100-£120/$150-$210

Midge

2 Crumbs

Designer:
Jean Walmsley Heap

Size:
3″

Production Period:
1956-1965

Market Value:
£150-£200/$225-$350

Picture
Unavailable

Midge

3 Crumbs

Designer:
Jean Walmsley Heap

Size:
3″

Production Period:
1956-1965

Market Value:
£200-£300/$300-$525

Midge

Picnic

Designer:
Jean Walmsley Heap

Size:
4″

Production Period:
1965-1999

Market Value:
£20-£30/$30-$53

Mike

Designer:
Doreen Noel Roberts

Size:
5″

Production Period:
1994-Cur

Market Value:
RRP

Mike

Designer:
Doreen Noel Roberts

Size:
5″

Production Period:
1994-Cur

Market Value:
RRP

Millennium Queen

Designer:
Doreen Noel Roberts

Production Period:
1999-2000

Market Value:
£200-£300/$300-$525

Moppit

Designer:
Jean Walmsley Heap

Size:
4″

Production Period:
1996-Cur

Market Value:
RRP

Moppit

Lime green colourway made for the Canadian Market 200 made

Designer:
Jean Walmsley Heap

Size:
4″

Production Period:
1996-1997

Market Value:
£500-£700/$750-$1225

Morris

Designer:
TG

Size:
4″

Production Period:
2001-Cur

Market Value:
RRP

Mother

Designer:
Jean Walmsley Heap

Size:
8″

Production Period:
1956-1978

Market Value:
£200-£300/$300-$525

Picture
Unavailable

Mother

Scalloped skirt

Designer:
Jean Walmsley Heap

Size:
8″

Production Period:
1956-1960

Market Value:
£300-£400 / $450-$700

Mother

Fringing to Shawl

Designer:
Jean Walmsley Heap

Size:
8″

Production Period:
1956-1960

Market Value:
£300-£400 / $450-$700

Mother

Tassels to Shawl

Designer:
Jean Walmsley Heap

Size:
8″

Production Period:
1956-1960

Market Value:
£300-£400 / $450-$700

Mother

Thin Neck

Designer:
Jean Walmsley Heap

Size:
8″

Production Period:
1956 only

Market Value:
£250-£350 / $375-$613

Mother

Thin Neck

Designer:
Jean Walmsley Heap

Size:
8″

Production Period:
1956 only

Market Value:
£250-£350 / $375-$613

Mother and Baby

Designer:
Jean Walmsley Heap

Size:
8″

Production Period:
1977-Cur

Market Value:
RRP

Muncher

Designer:
Doreen Noel Roberts

Size:
5″

Production Period:
1965-1983

Market Value:
£60-£100/$90-$175

New Boy

Designer:
Doreen Noel Roberts

Size:
4″

Production Period:
1990-1999

Market Value:
£30-£50/$45-$88

Nipper

Designer:
Doreen Noel Roberts

Size:
4″

Production Period:
1981-1989

Market Value:
£70-£100/$105-$175

Noel

Designer:
Doreen Noel Roberts

Size:
4″

Production Period:
1997-Cur

Market Value:
RRP

Old Bill

Designer:
TG

Size:
4″

Production Period:
2002-Cur

Market Value:
RRP

Oliver

Designer:
Doreen Noel Roberts

Size:
4″

Production Period:
1984-1995

Market Value:
£45-£60/$68-$105

Parsley

Designer:
Doreen Noel Roberts

Size:
4″

Production Period:
1987-Cur

Market Value:
RRP

Peeps

Designer:
Jean Walmsley Heap

Size:
4″

Production Period:
1966-2003

Market Value:
£12-£18/$18-$32

Peeps

One-off

Designer:
Jean Walmsley Heap

Size:
4″

Production Period:
1966-2003

Market Value:
£12-£18/$18-$32

Pendelfin Pete

Designer:
Doreen Noel Roberts

Size:
5″

Production Period:
1999-Cur

Market Value:
RRP

Pendelfin Pete

Canadian model

Designer:
Doreen Noel Roberts

Market Value:
£200-£300/$300-$525

Pepper

Designer:
Doreen Noel Roberts

Size:
3″

Production Period:
1995-2001

Market Value:
£20-£30/$30-$53

Phumf

Designer:
Doreen Noel Roberts

Size:
4″

Production Period:
1967-1985

Market Value:
£50-£80/$75-$140

Picnic Basket

Designer:
Jean Walmsley Heap

Size:
2″

Production Period:
1966-1968

Market Value:
£300-£500/$450-$875

Pie Face

Designer:
Doreen Noel Roberts

Size:
4″

Production Period:
1966-1987

Market Value:
£60-£80/$90-$140

Pilgrim

American Exclusive

Designer:
TG

Size:
5″

Production Period:
2001-2002

Market Value:
£100-£150/$150-$263

Pipkin

Designer:
Jean Walmsley Heap

Size:
4″

Production Period:
1994-2001

Market Value:
£20-£40/$30-$70

Pirate Patch

Designer:
TG

Size:
4″

Production Period:
1999-Cur

Market Value:
RRP

Pookie Style

Dungarees - Father

Designer:

Size:
-

Production Period:
1954-1955

Market Value:
£800-£1200/$1200-$2100

Poppet

2 or 3 Weaves

Designer:
Doreen Noel Roberts

Size:
4″

Production Period:
1964-2003

Market Value:
£20-£30/$30-$53

Postie

Designer:
TG

Size:
4″

Production Period:
2001-Cur

Market Value:
RRP

Rambler

Red

Designer:
Doreen Noel Roberts

Size:
4″

Production Period:
1991-2003

Market Value:
£20-£30/$30-$53

Rambler

Green

Designer:
Doreen Noel Roberts

Size:
4″

Production Period:
1991-2003

Market Value:
£20-£30/$30-$53

Rambler

Yellow

Designer:
Doreen Noel Roberts

Size:
4″

Production Period:
1991-2003

Market Value:
£20-£30/$30-$53

Rambler

Speckled hat (Limited edition of 500) (Scottish Rambler)

Designer:
Doreen Noel Roberts

Size:
4″

Production Period:
1998 only

Market Value:
£150-£200/$225-$350

Robert

Satchel

Designer:
Jean Walmsley Heap

Size:
5″

Production Period:
1956-1967

Market Value:
£200-£300/$300-$525

Robert

Satchel

Designer:
Jean Walmsley Heap

Size:
5″

Production Period:
1956-1967

Market Value:
£200-£300/$300-$525

Robert

Lollipop

Designer:
Jean Walmsley Heap

Size:
5″

Production Period:
1967-1979

Market Value:
£100-£200/$150-$350

Robin

Designer:
Doreen Noel Roberts

Size:
4″

Production Period:
2002-Cur

Market Value:
RRP

Rocky

1st version

Designer:
Jean Walmsley Heap

Size:
5″

Production Period:
1959-1978

Market Value:
£40-£60/$60-$105

Rocky

Shoes & Hat

Designer:
Jean Walmsley Heap

Size:
4″

Production Period:
1978-1997

Market Value:
£15-£20/$23-$35

Rolly

Designer:
Jean Walmsley Heap

Size:
4″

Production Period:
1959-1997

Market Value:
£18-£25/$27-$44

Rolly

Designer:
Jean Walmsley Heap

Size:
4″

Production Period:
1959-1997

Market Value:
£18-£25/$27-$44

Rolly

Designer:
Jean Walmsley Heap

Size:
4″

Production Period:
1959-1997

Market Value:
£18-£25/$27-$44

Rolly

Designer:
Jean Walmsley Heap

Size:
4″

Production Period:
1959-1997

Market Value:
£18-£25/$27-$44

Rosa

Designer:
Jean Walmsley Heap

Size:
4″

Production Period:
1982-1998

Market Value:
£40-£60/$60-$105

Rosa

Blue

Designer:
Jean Walmsley Heap

Size:
4″

Production Period:
1982-1984

Market Value:
£150-£200/$225-$350

Rosa

Black colourway 1 only known

Designer:
Jean Walmsley Heap

Size:
4″

Market Value:
£700-£1000/$1050-$1750

Rosa

Green

Designer:
Jean Walmsley Heap

Size:
4″

Production Period:
1982-1984

Market Value:
£180-£240/$270-$420

Rosa

Turquoise

Designer:
Jean Walmsley Heap

Size:
4″

Production Period:
1982-1984

Market Value:
£180-£240/$270-$420

Sandie

Designer:
Jean Walmsley Heap

Size:
4″

Production Period:
1997-Cur

Market Value:
RRP

Sandie

Special edition (Welsh Flag) 500 made

Designer:
Jean Walmsley Heap

Size:
4″

Production Period:
2001

Market Value:
£120-£200/$180-$350

Picture Unavailable

Sandie

Special edition (Blue Anchor) only 5 made

Designer:
Jean Walmsley Heap

Size:
4″

Production Period:
2001-2001

Market Value:
£200-£300/$300-$525

Scoffer

Designer:
Doreen Noel Roberts

Size:
4″

Production Period:
1991-2002

Market Value:
£30-£40/$45-$70

Scout

Designer:
Doreen Noel Roberts

Size:
5″Long

Production Period:
1992-2003

Market Value:
£30-£40/$45-$70

Scout

Special edition (Two Sausages) 500 made

Designer:
Doreen Noel Roberts

Size:
5″

Production Period:
1999-1999

Market Value:
£120-£200/$180-$350

Scrumpy

Designer:
Jean Walmsley Heap

Size:
4″

Production Period:
1985-2002

Market Value:
£20-£40/$30-$70

Sergeant Cuff

Designer:
TG

Size:
4″

Production Period:
2002-Cur

Market Value:
RRP

Shanty

Designer:
TG

Size:
4″

Production Period:
2000-Cur

Market Value:
RRP

Sheriff

Designer:
TG

Size:
4″

Production Period:
2000-Cur

Market Value:
RRP

Shiner

Designer:
Jean Walmsley Heap

Size:
4″

Production Period:
1960-1967

Market Value:
£300-£400/$450-$700

Shiner

Designer:
Jean Walmsley Heap

Size:
4″

Production Period:
1960-1967

Market Value:
£300-£400/$450-$700

Shrimpy

Designer:
Jean Walmsley Heap

Size:
4″

Production Period:
1998-Cur

Market Value:
RRP

Sledger

Designer:
Doreen Noel Roberts

Size:
4″

Production Period:
1998-Cur

Market Value:
RRP

Sledger

Designer:
Doreen Noel Roberts

Size:
4"

Production Period:
1998-Cur

Market Value:
RRP

Snuggles

Designer:
Jean Walmsley Heap

Size:
4"

Production Period:
1958-Cur

Market Value:
RRP

Snuggles

Designer:
Jean Walmsley Heap

Size:
4"

Production Period:
1958-Cur

Market Value:
RRP

Snuggles

Designer:
Jean Walmsley Heap

Size:
4"

Production Period:
1958-Cur

Market Value:
RRP

Snuggles

(Awake)

Designer:
Jean Walmsley Heap

Size:
4"

Production Period:
1991-2000

Market Value:
£30-£40/$45-$70

Solo

Designer:
Doreen Noel Roberts

Size:
4"

Production Period:
1985-1993

Market Value:
£50-£80/$75-$140

Solo

Black colourway, one only known

Designer:
Doreen Noel Roberts

Size:
4"

Market Value:
£700-£1000/$1050-$1750

Spud

Designer:
Doreen Noel Roberts

Size:
5"

Production Period:
1997-Cur

Market Value:
RRP

Squeezy

Designer:
Jean Walmsley Heap

Size:
3"

Production Period:
1960-1970

Market Value:
£200-£300/$300-$525

Striker

Canadian edition 200 made

Size:
4"

Production Period:
2001-2001

Market Value:
£80-£120/$120-$210

Striker

England

Size:
4"

Production Period:
2001-Cur

Market Value:
RRP

Striker

Scotland 500 made

Size:
4"

Production Period:
2001-2001

Market Value:
£80-£120/$120-$210

Striker

Burnley

Size:
4″

Production Period:
2002-2002

Market Value:
£80-£120/$120-$210

Striker

Gateshead edition 200 made

Size:
4″

Production Period:
2001-2001

Market Value:
£80-£120/$120-$210

Striker

Littlehampton edition 200 made

Size:
4″

Production Period:
2001-2001

Market Value:
£80-£120/$120-$210

Striker

Mablethorpe edition 200 made

Size:
4″

Production Period:
2001-2001

Market Value:
£80-£120/$120-$210

Striker

Colourway 1 only

Size:
4″

Production Period:
2001-2001

Market Value:
£80-£120/$120-$210

Sunny

Designer:
Doreen Noel Roberts

Size:
4″

Production Period:
1992-Cur

Market Value:
RRP

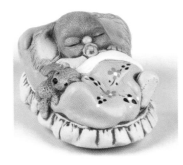

Sweep

Designer:
TG

Size:
4″

Production Period:
2001-Cur

Market Value:
RRP

Teddy

Designer:
Doreen Noel Roberts

Size:
4″

Production Period:
1995-Cur

Market Value:
RRP

Teddy

Green colourway

Designer:
Doreen Noel Roberts

Size:
3″

Market Value:
£0/$0

Tennyson

Designer:
Doreen Noel Roberts

Size:
4″

Production Period:
1987-1994

Market Value:
£50-£80/$75-$140

The Buffet

Ltd edition piece of 1000

Designer:
Jean Walmsley Heap

Size:
5″

Production Period:
2002

Market Value:
£100-£150/$150-$263

The Graduate

Designer:
TG

Size:
5″

Production Period:
2000-Cur

Market Value:
RRP

Thumper

Designer:
Jean Walmsley Heap

Size:
4″

Production Period:
1967-Cur

Market Value:
RRP

Tiddler

Designer:
Doreen Noel Roberts

Size:
4″

Production Period:
1996-2002

Market Value:
£30-£50/$45-$88

Tippit

Designer:
Jean Walmsley Heap

Size:
3″

Production Period:
1995-2000

Market Value:
£30-£50/$45-$88

Totty

Designer:
Jean Walmsley Heap

Size:
4″

Production Period:
1971-1981

Market Value:
£60-£80/$90-$140

Toy-Tot

Designer:
Jean Walmsley Heap

Size:
4″

Production Period:
1999-Cur

Market Value:
RRP

Tripper

Designer:
Jean Walmsley Heap

Size:
4″

Production Period:
1997-Cur

Market Value:
RRP

Twins

Designer:
Jean Walmsley Heap

Size:
4"Long

Production Period:
1962-2003

Market Value:
£10-£20/$15-$35

Twins

Designer:
Jean Walmsley Heap

Size:
4"Long

Production Period:
1962-2003

Market Value:
£10-£20/$15-$35

Twister

Designer:
TG

Size:
4"

Production Period:
2003-Cur

Market Value:
RRP

Uncle Henry

Limited edition of 7000

Designer:
Jean Walmsley Heap

Size:
8"

Production Period:
1997-2000

Market Value:
£100-£150/$150-$263

Uncle Soames

Designer:
Jean Walmsley Heap

Size:
8"

Production Period:
1959-1985

Market Value:
£150-£250/$225-$438

Uncle Soames

Brown Trousers

Designer:
Jean Walmsley Heap

Size:
8"

Production Period:
1959 only

Market Value:
£500-£700/$750-$1225

Uncle Soames

Blue Trousers

Designer:
Jean Walmsley Heap

Size:
8″

Production Period:
1959 only

Market Value:
£500-£700/$750-$1225

Uncle Soames

Mushroom Trousers

Designer:
Jean Walmsley Heap

Size:
8″

Production Period:
1959-1961

Market Value:
£500-£700/$750-$1225

Uncle Soames

Painted shoes

Designer:
Jean Walmsley Heap

Size:
8″

Production Period:
1959-1961

Market Value:
£500-£700/$750-$1225

Vanilla

Designer:
Doreen Noel Roberts

Size:
3″

Production Period:
1993-Cur

Market Value:
RRP

Victoria

Introduced to celebrate the recovery of the fire

Designer:
Jean Walmsley Heap

Size:
3″

Production Period:
1986-Cur

Market Value:
RRP

Wakey

Designer:
Jean Walmsley Heap

Size:
4″Long

Production Period:
1958-2003

Market Value:
£10-£20/$15-$35

Whopper

Designer:
Doreen Noel Roberts

Size:
5″

Production Period:
1979-Cur

Market Value:
RRP

Whopper

Silver Brim

Designer:
Doreen Noel Roberts

Size:
5″

Market Value:
£50-£80/$75-$140

Wordsworth

Designer:
Doreen Noel Roberts

Size:
4″

Production Period:
1991-1993

Market Value:
£80-£120/$120-$210

Members Gifts and
Models of the Year

▶ ▶

Bellman

Membership Gift

Designer:
Jean Walmsley Heap

Size:
5″

Production Period:
Jan 95-Dec 96

Market Value:
£80-£100/$120-$175

Bosun

Model of the Year

Designer:
Doreen Noel Roberts

Size:
5″

Production Period:
1992-1993

Market Value:
£100-£150/$150-$263

Buttons

Membership Gift

Designer:
Doreen Noel Roberts

Size:
4″

Production Period:
Jan 1994-Dec 1994

Market Value:
£80-£120/$120-$210

Delia

Model of the Year

Designer:
Jean Walmsley Heap

Size:
4″

Production Period:
Jan 96-Mar 97

Market Value:
£70-£100/$105-$175

Georgie & Dragon

Model of the Year

Designer:
Doreen Noel Roberts

Size:
5″

Production Period:
Jan 95-Mar 96

Market Value:
£150-£200/$225-$350

Gramps

Model of the Year

Designer:
Jean Walmsley Heap

Size:
5″

Production Period:
Jan 98-Mar 99

Market Value:
£80-£120/$120-$210

Gran

Model of the Year

Designer:
Jean Walmsley Heap

Size:
5″

Production Period:
2000-Mar 2001

Market Value:
£50-£80/$75-$140

Herald

Founder Member

Designer:
Jean Walmsley Heap

Size:
4″

Production Period:
Oct 92-Dec 93

Market Value:
£120-£200/$180-$350

Little Hero

Membership Gift

Designer:
Doreen Noel Roberts

Size:
4″

Production Period:
2000

Market Value:
£30-£40/$45-$70

Little Tom

Membership Gift

Designer:
Jean Walmsley Heap

Size:
5″

Production Period:
Jan 97-Dec 97

Market Value:
£40-£60/$60-$105

Newsie

Membership Gift

Designer:
Doreen Noel Roberts

Size:
4″

Production Period:
Jan 1996-Dec 1996

Market Value:
£70-£100/$105-$175

Peggy

Membership Gift

Designer:
Jean Walmsley Heap

Size:
4″

Production Period:
Jan 01-Mar 02

Market Value:
£30-£40/$45-$70

Puffer

Model of the Year

Designer:
Jean Walmsley Heap

Size:
5″

Production Period:
1994 only

Market Value:
£120-£180/$180-$315

Raphael

Membership Gift

Designer:
Jean Walmsley Heap

Size:
4″

Production Period:
Jan 03-Mar 04

Market Value:
£30-£40/$45-$70

Romeo & Juliet

Model of the Year

Designer:
Doreen Noel Roberts

Size:
5″

Production Period:
2003-Mar 04

Market Value:
£40-£60/$60-$105

Splasher

Membership Gift

Designer:
TG

Size:
4″

Production Period:
Jan 02-Mar 03

Market Value:
£30-£40/$45-$70

Sudsey

Model of the Year

Designer:
Doreen Noel Roberts

Size:
4"

Production Period:
2001-Mar 02

Market Value:
£40-£60/$60-$105

The Gaffer

Model of the Year

Designer:
Jean Walmsley Heap

Size:
4"

Production Period:
2002-Mar 03

Market Value:
£30-£40/$45-$70

Tidy Patch

Membership Gift

Designer:
Doreen Noel Roberts

Size:
5"

Production Period:
Jan 98-Dec 98

Market Value:
£40-£60/$60-$105

Treasure

Model of the Year

Designer:
Doreen Noel Roberts

Size:
5"Wide

Production Period:
Jan 99-Mar 2000

Market Value:
£50-£80/$75-$140

Trove

Membership Gift

Designer:
Jean Walmsley Heap

Size:
5"

Production Period:
Jan 99-Dec 99

Market Value:
£40-£60/$60-$105

Woody

Model of the Year

Designer:
Doreen Noel Roberts

Size:
4"

Production Period:
Jan 97-Mar 98

Market Value:
£70-£100/$105-$175

Event Pieces

▶ ▶

Bodgit

Designer:
Jean Walmsley Heap

Size:
5"Wide

Production Period:
1996

Market Value:
£70-£100/$105-$175

Fortunella

Designer:
Doreen Noel Roberts

Size:
4"

Production Period:
2001

Market Value:
£40-£60/$60-$105

Gentleman Jack

Designer:
Doreen Noel Roberts

Size:
4"

Production Period:
1999-1999

Market Value:
£50-£100/$75-$175

Hilarious Harry

Designer:
Jean Walmsley Heap

Size:
5"

Production Period:
2000-2000

Market Value:
£50-£80/$75-$140

Rockafella

Designer:
Jean Walmsley Heap

Size:
5"Wide

Production Period:
1998

Market Value:
£50-£100/$75-$175

Runaway

Designer:
Doreen Noel Roberts

Size:
5"Wide

Production Period:
1995

Market Value:
£80-£120/$120-$210

Steamy Jean

Designer:
Jean Walmsley Heap

Size:
4"

Production Period:
2002-2002

Market Value:
£40-£60/$60-$105

Sylvana

Designer:
Doreen Noel Roberts

Size:
5"Wide

Production Period:
1997

Market Value:
£120-£180/$180-$315

Walmsley

Designer:
Jean Walmsley Heap

Size:
5"Wide

Production Period:
1994

Market Value:
£120-£200/$180-$350

Buildings and Accessories

▶ ▶

Apple Barrel

Designer:
Doreen Noel Roberts

Size:
2"Dia

Production Period:
1985-1992

Market Value:
£25-£40/$38-$70

Badges & Keyrings

Market Value:
RRP

Balcony Scene

Designer:
Doreen Noel Roberts

Size:
9"Long

Production Period:
1992-1998

Market Value:
£80-£120/$120-$210

Bandstand

Designer:
Jean Walmsley Heap

Size:
12"

Production Period:
1964-1973

Market Value:
£150-£200/$225-$350

Bandstand

Remodelled

Designer:
Jean Walmsley Heap

Size:
12"

Production Period:
1973-1999

Market Value:
£40-£60/$60-$105

Picture
Unavailable

Bath Tub

Designer:
Doreen Noel Roberts

Size:
3"Long

Production Period:
1967-1975

Market Value:
£40-£60/$60-$105

Bath Tub

Remodelled

Designer:
Doreen Noel Roberts

Size:
3"Long

Production Period:
1982

Market Value:
£20-£30/$30-$53

Betsy Barge

Designer:
Jean Walmsley Heap

Size:
11"Long

Production Period:
1998-Cur

Market Value:
RRP

Cake Plate

Display piece

Designer:
Jean Walmsley Heap

Size:
2"Long

Production Period:
1966-1972

Market Value:
£120-£200/$180-$350

Cake Stand

Designer:
Jean Walmsley Heap

Size:
5"Long

Production Period:
1966-1972

Market Value:
£400-£600/$600-$1050

Camp Fire

*The Camp Fire model came with
smoke initially, however due to the
possible danger to children it
stopped being produced, the Camp
Fire is now sold without smoke*

Designer: Doreen Noel Roberts

Size: 5"Wide

Production Period: 1993-1999

Market Value: £50-£80/$75-$140

Camp Fire

Display piece
Designer:
Doreen Noel Roberts
Size:
5"Wide
Production Period:
1993-1999
Market Value:
£50-£80/$75-$140

Castle Tavern

Designer:
Doreen Noel Roberts
Size:
6"
Production Period:
1968-2001
Market Value:
£40-£60/$60-$105

Christmas Cabin

Designer:
Jean Walmsley Heap
Size:
6"
Production Period:
1996-Cur
Market Value:
RRP

Christmas Island

With Foliage
Designer:
Jean Walmsley Heap
Size:
15"
Production Period:
1996-2001
Market Value:
£60-£100/$90-$175

Christmas Scene

Limited Edition of 2000
Designer:
Doreen Noel Roberts
Size:
10"
Production Period:
1985-1986
Market Value:
£900-£1200/$1350-$2100

Cobble Cottage

Designer:
Doreen Noel Roberts
Size:
8"
Production Period:
1967-2001
Market Value:
£40-£60/$60-$105

Concert Stand

Designer:
Jean Walmsley Heap

Production Period:
2000-Cur

Market Value:
RRP

Curiosity Shop

Designer:
Jean Walmsley Heap

Size:
12″

Production Period:
1976-2001

Market Value:
£30-£40/$45-$70

Display Plaque

Market Value:
£100-£150/$150-$263

Display Sign

Market Value:
£200-£300/$300-$525

Display Stand

Signed

Market Value:
£0/$0

Easel Wedge

Designer:
Jean Walmsley Heap

Size:
3″Long

Production Period:
1968-1971

Market Value:
£150-£200/$225-$350

Fruit Shop

Designer:
Jean Walmsley Heap
Size:
11"Long
Production Period:
1968-2001
Market Value:
£30-£50/$45-$88

Grandstand

Designer:
Jean Walmsley Heap
Size:
15"Long
Production Period:
1961-1969
Market Value:
£150-£250/$225-$438

Grandstand

Remodelled
Designer:
Jean Walmsley Heap
Size:
15"Long
Production Period:
1990-1995
Market Value:
£80-£120/$120-$210

Jubilee Theatre

Designer:
Jean Walmsley Heap
Production Period:
2002
Market Value:
RRP

Lantern Stand

Designer:
Doreen Noel Roberts
Size:
11"
Production Period:
1985-1991
Market Value:
£80-£120/$120-$210

Large House

Similar to Pixie Bod House
Designer:
Jean Walmsley Heap
Size:
19"
Production Period:
1966-2003
Market Value:
£70-£100/$105-$175

Milk Jug Stand

Designer:
Jean Walmsley Heap

Size:
5"Long

Production Period:
1966-1972

Market Value:
£400-£600/$600-$1050

Millennium Nursery

Designer:
Jean Walmsley Heap

Production Period:
1999-2000

Market Value:
£200-£300/$300-$525

Model Stand

Rabbit

Designer:
Jean Walmsley Heap

Size:
10"Long

Production Period:
1960-1967

Market Value:
£250-£400/$375-$700

Model Stand

PenDelfin

Designer:
Jean Walmsley Heap

Size:
10"Long

Production Period:
1960-1967

Market Value:
£300-£500/$450-$875

Model Stand

Prototype

Designer:
Jean Walmsley Heap

Size:
9½" Long

Production Period:
1960 only

Market Value:
£600-£1000/$900-$1750

Old School House

Designer:
Jean Walmsley Heap

Size:
14"Wide

Production Period:
1989-Cur

Market Value:
RRP

Piano & Plant

Designer:
Doreen Noel Roberts

Size:
3"

Production Period:
1965-Cur

Market Value:
RRP

Picnic Island

Designer:
Jean Walmsley Heap

Size:
11"Long

Production Period:
1985-Cur

Market Value:
RRP

Picnic Island

Black kettle

Designer:
Jean Walmsley Heap

Size:
11"Long

Production Period:
1985-Cur

Market Value:
RRP

Picnic Stand

Designer:
Jean Walmsley Heap

Size:
2"Long

Production Period:
1965-1985

Market Value:
£100-£150/$150-$263

Picnic Stand

Black kettle

Designer:
Jean Walmsley Heap

Size:
2"Long

Production Period:
1965-1985

Market Value:
£100-£150/$150-$263

Picnic Table

Designer:
Jean Walmsley Heap

Size:
3"

Production Period:
1967-1972

Market Value:
£250-£300/$375-$525

Raft

Designer:
Jean Walmsley Heap

Size:
7"Long

Production Period:
1983-1997

Market Value:
£60-£100/$90-$175

Robins Cave

Designer:
Doreen Noel Roberts

Size:
8"Long

Production Period:
1995-1999

Market Value:
£70-£100/$105-$175

Shrimp Stand

Designer:
Doreen Noel Roberts

Size:
10"Long

Production Period:
1966-1982

Market Value:
£80-£120/$120-$210

The Caravan

Designer:
Doreen Noel Roberts

Size:
11"

Production Period:
1976-Cur

Market Value:
RRP

The Jetty

Designer:
Jean Walmsley Heap

Size:
14"Dia

Production Period:
1979-Cur

Market Value:
RRP

The Kitchen

Designer:
Jean Walmsley Heap

Size:
8"

Production Period:
1995-Cur

Market Value:
RRP

The Orchard

Designer:
Jean Walmsley Heap

Production Period:
2001-Cur

Market Value:
RRP

Timber Stand

Designer:
Doreen Noel Roberts

Size:
10"Long

Production Period:
1966-1982

Market Value:
£80-£120/$120-$210

Timber Stand

Green colourway

Designer:
Doreen Noel Roberts

Size:
10"Long

Production Period:
1966-1982

Market Value:
£100-£150/$150-$263

Toyshop

Designer:
Doreen Noel Roberts

Size:
11"Wide

Production Period:
1992-2000

Market Value:
£50-£100/$75-$175

Tree Trunk Stool

Designer:
Jean Walmsley Heap

Size:
11"Long

Production Period:
1965

Market Value:
£150-£200/$225-$350

Village Pond

Red boots, colour change 100 made

Designer:
Jean Walmsley Heap

Production Period:
2001

Market Value:
£170-£240/$255-$420

Wall Plaques & Ornamental Ware

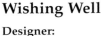

Wishing Well

Designer:
Jean Walmsley Heap

Size:
8"Long

Production Period:
1994-Cur

Market Value:
RRP

Bobbin Woman Figure

Only 2 made

Designer:
Jean Walmsley Heap

Size:
5"

Production Period:
1955-1959

Market Value:
£2000-£3000/$3000-$5250

Cauldron Witch Figure

Designer:
Jean Walmsley Heap

Size:
5"

Production Period:
1953-1959

Market Value:
£600-£800/$900-$1400

Cauldron Witch Figure

Colourway

Designer:
Jean Walmsley Heap

Size:
5"

Production Period:
1953-1959

Market Value:
£600-£800/$900-$1400

Cornish Prayer Figure

Designer:
Jean Walmsley Heap

Size:
4"

Production Period:
1962-1965

Market Value:
£500-£700/$750-$1225

Cyril Squirrel

Designer:
Doreen Noel Roberts

Size:
7″

Production Period:
1963-1965

Market Value:
£1200-£1800/$1800-$3150

Daisy Duck

Designer:
Jean Walmsley Heap

Size:
6″

Production Period:
1955-1958

Market Value:
£1500-£2000/$2250-$3500

Desmond Duck

Designer:
Jean Walmsley Heap

Size:
6″

Production Period:
1955-1958

Market Value:
£1500-£2000/$2250-$3500

Dodger

Gallery Series

Designer:
Jean Walmsley Heap

Size:
3″x 4″

Production Period:
1968-1971

Market Value:
£400-£600/$600-$1050

Dog with Scarf and Beret

Designer:
Jean Walmsley Heap

Size:
5″

Production Period:
1960-1962

Market Value:
£1200-£1800/$1800-$3150

Dog with Scarf and Beret

Designer:
Jean Walmsley Heap

Size:
5″

Production Period:
1960-1962

Market Value:
£1200-£1800/$1800-$3150

Dragon Ring Candle Holders

Designer:
Jean Walmsley Heap

Size:
4"Dia

Production Period:
1954-1958

Market Value:
£500-£800/$750-$1400

Fairy Jardiniere with Bookends

Designer:
Jean Walmsley Heap

Size:
5"

Production Period:
1954-1958

Market Value:
£3000-£5000/$4500-$8750

Fairy Jardiniere with Bookends

Designer:
Jean Walmsley Heap

Size:
5"

Production Period:
1954-1958

Market Value:
£3000-£5000/$4500-$8750

Picture
Unavailable

Fairy Shop Plaque

Coloured

Designer:
Jean Walmsley Heap

Size:
16"x10.5"

Production Period:
1954-1958

Market Value:
£1500-£2500/$2250-$4375

Fairy Shop Plaque

Brown Glaze (Ivory finish)

Designer:
Jean Walmsley Heap

Size:
16"x10.5"

Production Period:
1954-1958

Market Value:
£800-£1200/$1200-$2100

Gallery Series Display

Designer:
Jean Walmsley Heap

Size:
3"x 4"

Production Period:
1968-1971

Market Value:
£400-£600/$600-$1050

Gallery Series Display

Paper Front

Designer:
Jean Walmsley Heap

Size:
3"x 4"

Production Period:
1968-1971

Market Value:
£400-£600/$600-$1050

Manx Kitten

Designer:
Jean Walmsley Heap

Size:
4"

Production Period:
1956-1958

Market Value:
£1500-£2000/$2250-$3500

Mouse House Match Holder

Designer:
Doreen Noel Roberts

Size:
3"

Production Period:
1964-1969

Market Value:
£400-£600/$600-$1050

Mouse House Match Holder

Green colourway

Designer:
Doreen Noel Roberts

Size:
3"

Production Period:
1964-1969

Market Value:
£400-£600/$600-$1050

Old Adam

Figure

Designer:
Jean Walmsley Heap

Size:
7"

Production Period:
1955-1956

Market Value:
£1200-£1800/$1800-$3150

Old Adam

Lamp (limited number)

Designer:
Jean Walmsley Heap

Size:
16"

Production Period:
1955-1956

Market Value:
£1500-£2000/$2250-$3500

Old Meg Plaque

Designer:
Jean Walmsley Heap

Size:
8″

Production Period:
1953-1954

Market Value:
£5000-£8000 / $7500-$14000

Oracle

Very rare Owl made for photography of DNR book, sold at auction on behalf of charity. One only

Designer:
Doreen Noel Roberts

Market Value:
£4000-£6000 / $6000-$10500

Pendle Witch Plaque

Designer:
Jean Walmsley Heap

Size:
8″

Production Period:
1953-1957

Market Value:
£1500-£2000 / $2250-$3500

Pieface

Gallery Series

Designer:
Doreen Noel Roberts

Size:
3″ x 4″

Production Period:
1968-1971

Market Value:
£400-£600 / $600-$1050

Pixie House Plaque

Designer:
Jean Walmsley Heap

Size:
8″

Production Period:
1953-1958

Market Value:
£1800-£2500 / $2700-$4375

Pooch

Designer:
Doreen Noel Roberts

Size:
4″Long

Production Period:
1962-1987

Market Value:
£40-£60 / $60-$105

Pooch

Designer:
Doreen Noel Roberts

Size:
4"Long

Production Period:
1962-1987

Market Value:
£40-£60/$60-$105

Poppet

Gallery Series

Designer:
Doreen Noel Roberts

Size:
3"x 4"

Production Period:
1968-1971

Market Value:
£400-£600/$600-$1050

Rabbit Bookends

Designer:
Jean Walmsley Heap

Size:
5"

Production Period:
1958-1965

Market Value:
£3000-£5000/$4500-$8750

Picture
Unavailable

Rheingold Lamp

Wooden Base

Designer:
Jean Walmsley Heap

Production Period:
1954-1956

Market Value:
£1500-£2000/$2250-$3500

Rheingold Lamp

Stone Craft Base

Designer:
Jean Walmsley Heap

Production Period:
1954-1958

Market Value:
£1500-£2000/$2250-$3500

Robert

Gallery Series

Designer:
Jean Walmsley Heap

Size:
3"x 4"

Production Period:
1968-1971

Market Value:
£400-£600/$600-$1050

Romeo & Juliet Wall Plaques

Coloured

Designer:
Jean Walmsley Heap

Size:
8″

Production Period:
1957-1959

Market Value:
£1500-£2500/$2250-$4375

Romeo & Juliet Wall Plaques

Ivory

Designer:
Jean Walmsley Heap

Size:
8″

Production Period:
1957-1959

Market Value:
£1500-£2500/$2250-$4375

Shaggy Dog Wall Plaque

Designer:
Jean Walmsley Heap

Size:
5″

Production Period:
1955-1958

Market Value:
£1000-£1200/$1500-$2100

Tammy Puppy

Designer:
Jean Walmsley Heap

Size:
3″

Production Period:
1957-1987

Market Value:
£40-£60/$60-$105

Tammy Puppy

Designer:
Jean Walmsley Heap

Size:
3″

Production Period:
1957-1987

Market Value:
£40-£60/$60-$105

Tipsy Witch Figure

Designer:
Jean Walmsley Heap

Size:
5″

Production Period:
1953-1959

Market Value:
£400-£600/$600-$1050

Miniature "A" Plaques
▶▶

Wakey

Gallery Series

Designer:
Doreen Noel Roberts

Size:
3" x 4"

Production Period:
1968-1971

Market Value:
£400-£600/$600-$1050

Balloon Woman Wall Figure

Designer:
Jean Walmsley Heap

Size:
3"

Production Period:
1955-1956

Market Value:
£500-£700/$750-$1225

Bellman Wall Figure

Designer:
Jean Walmsley Heap

Size:
3"

Production Period:
1955-1956

Market Value:
£500-£700/$750-$1225

Elf Wall Figure

Designer:
Jean Walmsley Heap

Size:
3"

Production Period:
1955-1956

Market Value:
£500-£700/$750-$1225

Flying Witch Wall Figure

Designer:
Jean Walmsley Heap

Size:
3"

Production Period:
1955-1956

Market Value:
£500-£700/$750-$1225

Herald Wall Figure

Designer:
Jean Walmsley Heap

Size:
3″

Production Period:
1955-1956

Market Value:
£500-£700/$750-$1225

Phynnodderee (Manx Pixie)

Designer:
Jean Walmsley Heap

Size:
3″

Production Period:
1955-1956

Market Value:
£800-£1200/$1200-$2100

Scrooge Wall Figure

Designer:
Jean Walmsley Heap

Size:
3″

Production Period:
1955-1956

Market Value:
£500-£700/$750-$1225

Standing Witch Figure

Designer:
Jean Walmsley Heap

Size:
3″

Production Period:
1955-1956

Market Value:
£500-£700/$750-$1225

Toper Wall Figure

Designer:
Jean Walmsley Heap

Size:
3″

Production Period:
1955-1956

Market Value:
£500-£700/$750-$1225

Miniature "B" Plaques

▶ ▶

Little Bo Peep

Designer:
Jean Walmsley Heap

Size:
5"

Production Period:
1956-1959

Market Value:
£400-£600/$600-$1050

Little Jack Horner

Deep Relief Nursery Rhyme Character

Designer:
Jean Walmsley Heap

Size:
5"

Production Period:
1956-1959

Market Value:
£400-£600/$600-$1050

Mary Mary

Deep Relief Nursery Rhyme Character

Designer:
Jean Walmsley Heap

Size:
5"

Production Period:
1956-1959

Market Value:
£400-£600/$600-$1050

Miss Muffet

Deep Relief Nursery Rhyme Character

Designer:
Jean Walmsley Heap

Size:
5"

Production Period:
1956-1959

Market Value:
£400-£600/$600-$1050

Tom the Pipers Son

Deep Relief Nursery Rhyme Character

Designer:
Jean Walmsley Heap

Size:
5"

Production Period:
1956-1959

Market Value:
£400-£600/$600-$1050

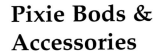

Wee Willie Winkie

Deep Relief Nursery Rhyme Character

Designer:
Jean Walmsley Heap

Size:
5″

Production Period:
1956-1959

Market Value:
£500-£700/$750-$1225

All Pixie Bods

Designer:
Jean Walmsley Heap

Size:
4″

Production Period:
1965-1967

Market Value:
£400-£600/$600-$1050

All Pixie Bods

Designer:
Jean Walmsley Heap

Size:
4″

Production Period:
1965-1967

Market Value:
£400-£600/$600-$1050

Girl Bod

Designer:
Jean Walmsley Heap

Size:
5″

Production Period:
1965-1967

Market Value:
£500-£700/$750-$1225

Girl Bod

Designer:
Jean Walmsley Heap

Size:
5″

Production Period:
1965-1967

Market Value:
£500-£700/$750-$1225

Pixie Bod Caravan

Approx. 14 issued

Designer:
Jean Walmsley Heap

Size:
12"

Production Period:
1965-1965

Market Value:
£3000-£5000/$4500-$8750

Pixie Bod House

Display piece. This was later produced as the Large House for the Rabbit family. See also ?????

Designer:
Jean Walmsley Heap

Size:
19"

Production Period:
1965 only

Market Value:
£3000-£5000/$4500-$8750

PenDelfin Mouse Family

▶ ▶

The first models of the mice where produced with a grey glaze. Because they stood out from the rabbits the glaze was changed to brown and the mouse family then blended in more with the rabbit collections.

Father Mouse

Brown

Designer:
Jean Walmsley Heap

Size:
4½"

Production Period:
1961-1966

Market Value:
£400-£600/$600-$1050

Father Mouse

Grey

Designer:
Jean Walmsley Heap

Size:
4½"

Production Period:
1961-1966

Market Value:
£400-£600/$600-$1050

Lollipop Mouse

Brown

Designer:
Jean Walmsley Heap

Size:
4½″

Production Period:
1961-1966

Market Value:
£400-£600 / $600-$1050

Lollipop Mouse

Grey

Designer:
Jean Walmsley Heap

Size:
4½″

Production Period:
1961-1966

Market Value:
£400-£600 / $600-$1050

Mother Mouse

Brown

Designer:
Jean Walmsley Heap

Size:
4½″

Production Period:
1961-1966

Market Value:
£400-£600 / $600-$1050

The Metallion Range

▶ ▶

Mother Mouse

Grey

Designer:
Jean Walmsley Heap

Size:
4½″

Production Period:
1961-1966

Market Value:
£400-£600 / $600-$1050

Bronze Column

Designer:
Doreen Noel Roberts

Production Period:
1980-1985

Market Value:
£500-£700 / $750-$1225

Bronze Plant Pot

Designer:
Doreen Noel Roberts

Production Period:
1980-1985

Market Value:
£400-£600/$600-$1050

Dove Chalice

Designer:
Doreen Noel Roberts

Size:
14″

Production Period:
1980-1985

Market Value:
£300-£500/$450-$875

Dragon Candle Holder

Designer:
Jean Walmsley Heap

Size:
5″

Production Period:
1980-1985

Market Value:
£150-£250/$225-$438

Dragon Flower Holder

Designer:
Jean Walmsley Heap

Size:
8″

Production Period:
1980-1985

Market Value:
£200-£400/$300-$700

Dragon Flower Holder

White

Designer:
Jean Walmsley Heap

Size:
8″

Production Period:
1980-1985

Market Value:
£200-£400/$300-$700

Elf Tree Candle Holder

Designer:
Doreen Noel Roberts

Size:
4″

Production Period:
1980-1985

Market Value:
£150-£250/$225-$438

Elf Tree Flower Holder

Designer:
Doreen Noel Roberts

Size:
4"

Production Period:
1980-1985

Market Value:
£300-£500/$450-$875

Father Rabbit

Designer:
Jean Walmsley Heap

Size:
7"

Production Period:
1980-1985

Market Value:
£150-£250/$225-$438

Father Rabbit

Designer:
Jean Walmsley Heap

Size:
7"

Production Period:
1980-1985

Market Value:
£150-£250/$225-$438

Flying Witch Wall Plaque

Designer:
Jean Walmsley Heap

Size:
8"Long

Production Period:
1980-1985

Market Value:
£500-£800/$750-$1400

Ivy Leaf Candlestick

Designer:
Doreen Noel Roberts

Size:
4"

Production Period:
1980-1985

Market Value:
£80-£120/$120-$210

Ivy Leaf Posy Bowl

Designer:
Doreen Noel Roberts

Size:
7"Dia

Production Period:
1980-1985

Market Value:
£200-£300/$300-$525

Mother and Baby Rabbit

Designer:
Jean Walmsley Heap

Size:
7″

Production Period:
1980-1985

Market Value:
£150-£250/$225-$438

Mother and Baby Rabbit

Designer:
Jean Walmsley Heap

Size:
7″

Production Period:
1980-1985

Market Value:
£150-£250/$225-$438

Mouse House Candlestick

Designer:
Doreen Noel Roberts

Size:
3″-4″

Production Period:
1980-1985

Market Value:
£120-£180/$180-$315

Rabbit Bookends

Designer:
Jean Walmsley Heap

Size:
8″

Production Period:
1980-1985

Market Value:
£800-£1200/$1200-$2100

Shell Flower Holder

Designer:
Jean Walmsley Heap

Size:
7½″

Production Period:
1980-1985

Market Value:
£180-£240/$270-$420

Shell Flower Holder

Designer:
Jean Walmsley Heap

Size:
11½″

Production Period:
1980-1985

Market Value:
£300-£500/$450-$875

Sunflower Plinth

Designer:
Doreen Noel Roberts

Size:
6"Dia

Production Period:
1980-1985

Market Value:
£150-£250/$225-$438

Swan Child Wall Sculpture

Designer:
Doreen Noel Roberts

Size:
12"

Production Period:
1980-1985

Market Value:
£400-£600/$600-$1050

Limited Editions
▶ ▶

Leaping Salmon (250)

also produced in a Pewter Finish.

Designer:
Hugh Dereck

Size:
25"

Market Value:
£1200-£1800/$1800-$3150

Rose Dragon (100)

Designer:
Jean Walmsley Heap

Size:
18"

Market Value:
£1800-£2400/$2700-$4200

Rose Dragon

Prototype (Jeans original model)

Designer:
Jean Walmsley Heap

Size:
18"

Market Value:
£3000-£5000/$4500-$8750

Swan Child Wall Sculpture (2)

Ivory Finish

Designer:
Doreen Noel Roberts

Size:
12"

Market Value:
£500/$750

PenDelfin Charms

▶ ▶

These little miniature models of six of the rabbit characters made from solid Sterling Silver were made in Canada.

Approximately 300 sets were made and distributed to H. Birks Ltd in Canada and the United States. They were not produced in the United Kingdom due to the increase in Sterling Silver prices, which would have made the charms uneconomical to produce, therefore the line came out of production. The model Barney was not only produced in Sterling Silver but in 15 carat gold, six were made as a limited edition and are extremely rare.

Picture
Unavailable

Barney

Designer:
Doreen Noel Roberts

Size:
10mm

Production Period:
1979-1980

Market Value:
£100-£150/$150-$263

Bongo

Sterling Silver Range

Designer:
Jean Walmsley Heap

Market Value:
RRP

Bongo

14ct Gold Plated Charms

Designer:
Jean Walmsley Heap

Market Value:
RRP

Bracelet

Sterling Silver Range

Market Value:
RRP

Maud

Sterling Silver Range

Market Value:
RRP

Maud

14ct Gold Plated Charms

Market Value:
RRP

Midge

Size: 10mm

Production Period:
1979-1980

Market Value:
£100-£150/$150-$263

Muncher

Designer:
Doreen Noel Roberts

Size: 10mm

Production Period: 1979-1980

Market Value:
£100-£150/$150-$263

Phumf

Designer:
Doreen Noel Roberts

Size: 10mm

Production Period: 1979-1980

Market Value:
£100-£150/$150-$263

Silver Necklace

Sterling Silver Range

Market Value:
RRP

Squeezy

Sterling Silver Range

Designer:
Jean Walmsley Heap

Market Value:
RRP

Squeezy

14ct Gold Plated Charms

Designer:
Jean Walmsley Heap

Market Value:
RRP

Totty

Designer: Jean Walmsley Heap

Size:10mm

Production Period: 1979-1980

Market Value:
£100-£150/$150-$263

Collectors Plates

▶ ▶

Picture
Unavailable

Wakey

Size:
10mm

Production Period:
1979-1980

Market Value:
£100-£150/$150-$263

Caravan

Limited Edition of 7500

Size:
9"Dia

Production Period:
1990-Cur

Market Value:
RRP

Father

Limited Edition of 10,000

Designer:
Jean Walmsley Heap

Size:
9"Dia

Production Period:
1982-1984

Market Value:
£70-£100/$105-$175

Gingerbread Day

Limited Edition of 7500

Size:
9"Dia

Production Period:
1989-Cur

Market Value:
RRP

Mother & Baby

Limited Edition of 10,000

Size:
9"Dia

Production Period:
1982-1983

Market Value:
£200-£300/$300-$525

The Old Schoolhouse

Limited Edition of 7500

Size:
9"Dia

Production Period:
1992-Cur

Market Value:
RRP

Whopper

Limited Edtion of 7500

Designer:
Doreen Noel Roberts

Size:
9"Dia

Production Period:
1982-1985

Market Value:
£70-£100/$105-$175

Whopper

Fluted version - Prototype

Designer:
Doreen Noel Roberts

Size:
9"Dia

Production Period:
1982

Market Value:
£120-£180/$180-$315

China Wares

▶ ▶

Breakfast Sets

Pink or Blue

Production Period:
1992-Cur

Market Value:
RRP

Ginger Jar and Cover

Prototype

Market Value:
£0/$0

Mugs

Pink or Blue

Production Period:
1992-2001

Market Value:
£0/$0

Porringer Set

250 made

Designer:
Doreen Noel Roberts

Production Period:
1997 only

Market Value:
£50-£80/$75-$140

Staker Mugs

Set of 3 Pink/Blue

Production Period:
2001-Cur

Market Value:
RRP

Tea For One

Production Period:
2001-Cur

Market Value:
RRP

Tea For Two Set

Production Period:
1992-2001

Market Value:
£0/$0

Trinket Boxes

Small, Medium, Large

Production Period:
1992-Cur

Market Value:
RRP

Block Wall Mounted Pictures

▶▶

The Auction

Size:
14"x 20"

Production Period:
1989-1994

Market Value:
£40-£60/$60-$105

The Dance

Size:
14"x 20"

Production Period:
1989-1994

Market Value:
£40-£60/$60-$105

The Homestead

Size:
14"x 20"

Production Period:
1989-1994

Market Value:
£40-£60/$60-$105

Decoupage Pictures

▶▶

Picture Unavailable

The Famous Auction

Size:
10"x 11.75"

Production Period:
1998-1999

Market Value:
RRP

Picture Unavailable

Fun and Games at the Large House

Size:
10"x 11.75"

Production Period:
1998-1999

Market Value:
RRP

Picture Unavailable

The Workshop of Father Rabbit

Size:
10"x 11.75"

Production Period:
1998-1999

Market Value:
RRP

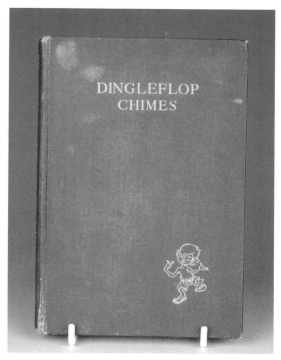

Dingleflop Chimes, *written and illustrated by Jean Walmsley Heap.*

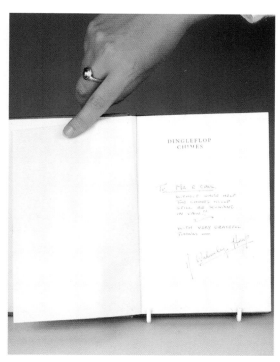

Inscription by Jean Walmsley Heap to Dingleflop

Dingleflop Moon, *written and illustrated by Jean*

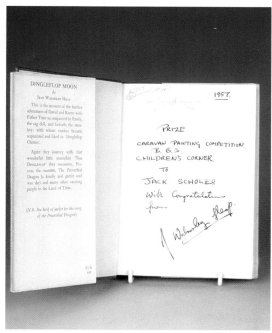

Inscription by Jean Walmsley Heap to Frontispiece

Pookie At The Seaside *story book by Ivy Wallace.*

Illustration from Eileen Graham's book The Pink Rabbit *by Jean Walmsley Heap, published by Candlelight Productions in 1948.*

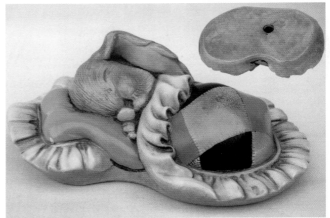

Large sleeping rabbit, similar to Snuggles, 10 inches long and base, NOT PenDelfin.

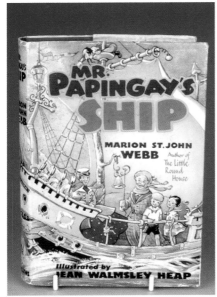

Illustrated by Jean Walmsley Heap Mr Papingay's Ship, *written by Marion St. John Webb.*

Pendelfin Art Work by Jean Walmsley Heap, £1000-£1500/$1995-$2995.

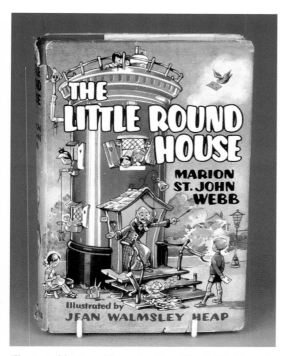

Illustrated by Jean Walmsley Heap The Little Round House, *written by Marion St. John Webb.*

Illustration from The Little Round House *by Jean Walmsley Heap*

Illustration from The Little Round House *by Jean Walmsley Heap*

Illustration from The Little Round House *by Jean Walmsley Heap*

Join our Family Circle

PenDelfin Times

PenDelfin International

United Kingdom £22.50 inc VAT
PENDELFIN FAMILY CIRCLE
Cameron Mill, Howsin Street, Burnley, Lancashire, England BB10 1PP
Tel: 01282 432301

America $30
The Family Circle of PenDelfin
230 Spring Street NW, Suite 1238
Atlanta, Georgia 30303
Freephone (US only) 1-800 872 4876
Contact: Susan Beard

Australia $55
PenDelfin Family Circle
Matthew Baldock Agencies
31 Massey St, Rossmoyne,
Western Australia 6148
Contact: Mr Matthew Baldock
Tel: (089) 457 9939

Canada $45
PenDelfin Family Circle
1250 Terwillegar Avenue, Oshawa,
Ontario, L1J 7A5, Canada
Contact: Tawni
Tel: 001 905 723 9940

Netherlands Hfl79.95
Harvest Collectables Guild
Van Utrechtweg 65,
2921 LN Krimpen a/d IJssel,
Netherlands.
Contact: Dhr O. C. Terlouw
Tel: 31-180 551844

Sweden Kr295
Svebi AB, Box 143,
S-562 02 Taberg
Sweden
Contact: Mrs. Irene Svensson
Tel: 036 656 90

Belgium & Luxembourg F1450
Sico PenDelfin Family Circle
Winkelstap 81, B-2900 Schoten
Tel: 03647 1761
Fax: 03647 1786
email: luc.sico@village.uunet.be

An invitation to Lovers of

PenDelfin

PenDelfin Pete designed by Doreen Noel Roberts is available exclusively to visitors to the Burnley Studio

---

BECOME a MEMBER of our FAMILY CIRCLE and you will enhance your collection becoming part of a growing family with other collectors who wish to share their joy and experiences collecting PENDELFIN.

◆ Membership Gift ◆

As an official MEMBER you will receive your MEMBERSHIP GIFT – a delightful character sculptured by DOREEN NOEL ROBERTS or JEAN WALMSLEY HEAP.

◆ Official Member Certificate ◆

You will receive your own Certificate to commemorate you being a member of our Circle.

◆ Club Newsletter ◆

The PENDELFIN TIMES will be sent to you THREE times per year keeping you up-to-date with all the news about your collection and informing you about any Special Events in your particular country.

◆ Membership Card ◆

You will receive your Official Card and your Redemption Certicate which entitles you to purchase the Exclusive Members Only Figurine by DOREEN NOEL ROBERTS or JEAN WALMSLEY HEAP from your PenDelfin stockist.

◆ Membership Draw ◆

Your name will be entered into our Year End Draw for a prize to be announced in the PENDELFIN TIMES.

ABOVE PRICES ARE FOR 1998 AND ARE SUBJECT TO CHANGE THEREAFTER

APPLICATION FORM

NAME
(BLOCK CAPITALS PLEASE)

ADDRESS

COUNTY

POSTCODE

PHONE NO.

EXISTING MEMBERSHIP NO.

FAVOURITE PENDELFIN RABBIT

Please make cheques payable to PenDelfin Family Circle and send to your own distributor listed above in *PenDelfin Times* to the value shown for your own country or deduct from my Mastercard / Visa / Switch card.

NUMBER

EXPIRY DATE

VALID FROM   ISSUE NO